DAVID SINDEN

ANTI JOURNAL

create outrageously

DAVID SINDEN   **NIKALAS CATLOW**

MACMILLAN

First published 2014 by Macmillan Children's Books
an imprint of Pan Macmillan
a division of Macmillan Publishers Limited
20 New Wharf Road, London N1 9RR
Associated companies throughout the world
www.panmacmillan.com

ISBN 978-1-4472-8879-4

3 5 7 9 8 6 4 2

A CIP catalogue record for this book is available from the British Library.

Printed and bound by CPI Group (UK) Ltd, Croydon CR0 4YY

DISCLAIMER:
ALWAYS EXERCISE CARE FOR YOURSELF
AND OTHERS WHILST USING THIS BOOK.
AVOID DOING ANYTHING DANGEROUS

WHAT IS
ANTI JOURNALING?

ANTI JOURNALING IS A
ROUTE TO CREATIVE DISCOVERY,
A WAY OF SEEING THINGS
DIFFERENTLY – IT'S JOURNALING
OUTSIDE THE BOX

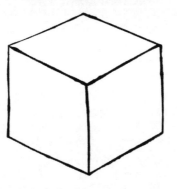

Write over this page, avoiding the box:
'I WILL NOT MAKE BORING ART'

THIS ANTI JOURNAL IS A PLACE
TO CREATE IN NEW WAYS . . .

THROW A WET TEABAG AT THIS PAGE
THEN FRAME THE CONSEQUENCES

ALLOW YOURSELF TO BE

Fill this with GARISH COLOUR

LET OUT YOUR FEELINGS ...

vent angrily here — decorate it happily

TURN THINGS ON
THEIR HEAD...

Cut up a photo and transform
it into an abstract composition

CHALLENGE ALL PRECONCEPTIONS OF ART

RUB this PAGE ON the GRASS

YOU WILL FIND FRESH MEANING...

OPEN AN UNWANTED BOOK AT RANDOM AND
CUT THE FIRST WORD FROM EACH line –
REARRANGE THEM

COVER EVERY INCH
OF THIS JOURNAL
AS YOU PLEASE –

iNlcudiNg its FRONT, BACK,
edges ANd tHis pAge

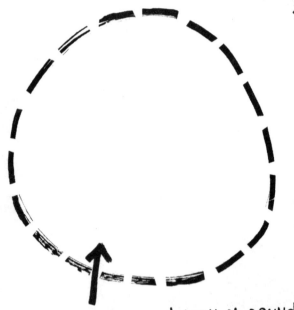

Cut tHis OUt ANd tURN it ROUNd.
Let it AFFeCt tHe pREViOUs pAge

MODIFY USING A MUG

Colours I LOVE

Colours I feel indifferent about

Colours I HATE

Add a piece of
coloured cardboard

Add a swatch of
fabric you dislike

Stain with something
from your kitchen

Explore art
tools and
mixed media

Tear this out and carry
it in your pocket until
an idea strikes

Fill using cosmetics

add lines from barcodes

pencil rub a texture

outline a small object from your drawer

arrange strands

build this up in 3-D

be random

REPEAT and ALTER

Fill with completely illegible

handwriting

CATALOGUE
INSIGNIFICANT
THINGS

PAiNT USiNG OBJECTS tHAT ROLL

be quiet with lines

BE LOUD WITH LINES

SEE MISTAKES AS OPPORTUNITIES –

continue this . . .

Completely fill this space with

BEAUTY

Sketch strangers

from behind

DESCRIBE YOURSELF
IN COLOUR

Create pets from pocket fluff

GIVE YOURSELF ADVICE

NOW IGNORE THIS AND DOODLE OVER IT

PATTERN WITH A PIN

PATTERN WITH A HOLE PUNCH

PRINT WITH junk

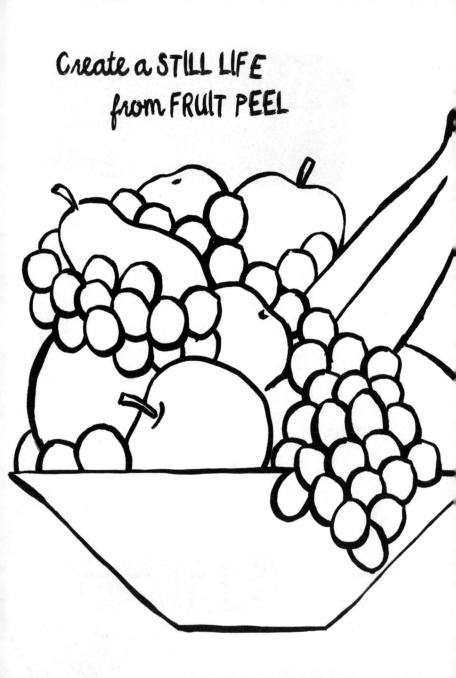

Create a STILL LIFE
from FRUIT PEEL

TWEET A page
FROM YOUR JOURNAL
#anti_journal

produce an ever-changing line

CREATE
AN IMAGE
FROM YOUR
PHONE
NUMBER

ADD BUBBLE WRAP

pop WHEN stressed

wipe YOUR FiNGeRS HERE AS AN
ABSTRACT impRESSiONiSt woUld

GO MAD WITH A STICK

SHOW OFF your
true colours

These are black words

REPEAT AND ALTER

make
EACH one
different

STITCH LINES

CAPTURE ENERGY

Reupholster this chair in real fabric

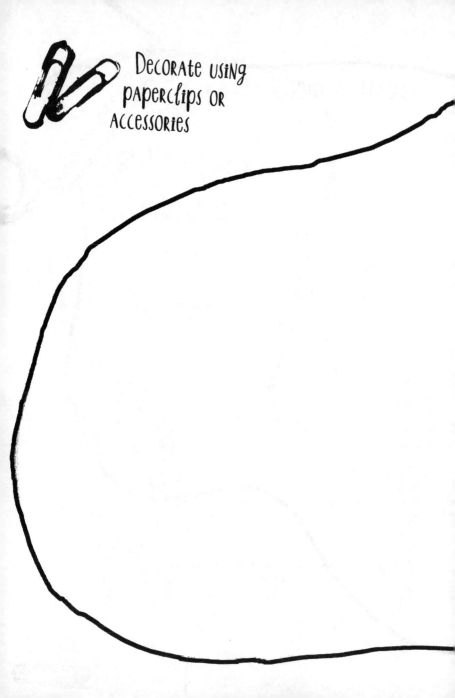

Decorate using
paperclips or
accessories

CREATE A MOOD BOARD FROM spillages

Perfect your pout

PASTE

IN

ANY

SECTION

OF A

MAGAZINE

BLACK

OUT

SOME

WORDS

LEAVE

SOME

Record your diet
through food packaging

 what the
BAD pen did:

glue in
something CUTE

SHOUT
COLOURFUL LANGUAGE

UGLIFY
BEAUTY

Radiate

A
SELFIE
DISGUISED

tweet this
#anti_journal

DIFFERENT SURFACES

CREATE ONLY WITH YOUR Feet

ASK PEOPLE TO
LEAVE A MARK
ON THIS PAGE

create a pattern
in staples

CHALK IT

cover this page with things that
will CHANGE
over time

test
the
P●SSiBiLiTies
OF AN
UNLIKELY
drawing TOOL

It's OK to potato stamp — you are never too old

Do something
so OUTRAGEOUS
you have to
cover it up

THE SAME VIEW . . .

... ON DIFFERENT DAYS

THE LAST THING ANYONE would expect HERE

WRITE A NOTE TO YOURSELF

Dear Past Me...

A KETCHUP-RELATED
CATASTROPHE

Make a spontaneous MARK
TURN IT into something

Use a store card
as a drawing tool

Don't hold back —
ATTACK!

TAKE AN UNUSUAL

POINT OF VIEW

DESIGN USING TAPE
OR STICKY THINGS

DRAW HOW YOU
drew Aged 4 ¾

BUILD A PATTERN FROM PATTERNS

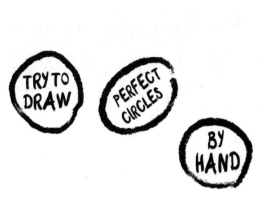

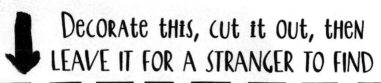

Decorate this, cut it out, then
LEAVE IT FOR A STRANGER TO FIND

- - - - - - - - - -

YOU HAVE FOUND
A BIT OF HAPPINESS

*If you're the happy finder,
tweet 'happy' #anti_journal*

Project shadows here.
Preserve them in any medium

colours here

RECORD A WALK
iN images
OR
oBJects

Phone someone you
haven't spoken to for a while.
Doodle while you talk

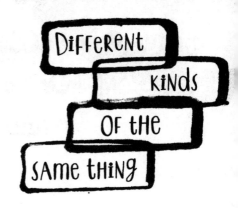

DIFFERENT KINDS OF THE SAME THING

DRAW WITH A FRIEND
using ONE PENCIL, holding it together and moving in tandem

EXPRESS
RHYTHM.
Make AN IMAGE
FROM
MUSIC

LIST THE
CONTENTS OF YOUR BAG

A LIST
THAT
DOESN'T
USE
WORDS

THINGS THAT HAVE
HAPPENED TO YOU
ONLY ONCE

MEMORIES EXPRESSED
AS SINGLE WORDS

THINGS YOU USED TO DO
THAT YOU DON'T ANY MORE

URGENT TO DO

A LIST WITH
NO CONNECTIONS

continue this...

Today is a blank page.
FILL IT VIBRANTLY

Stick an envelope here

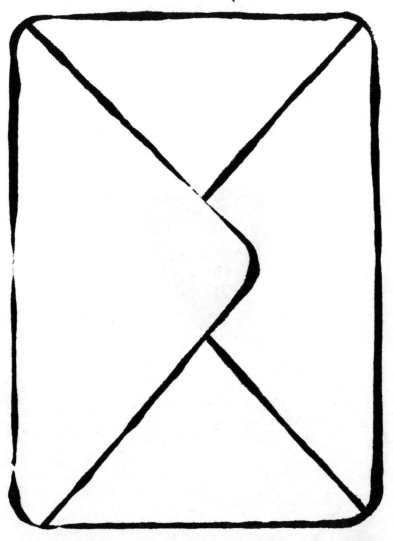

Gather ephemera to use in your work

CREATE
LOVE

OUTLINE the
SPACE BETWEEN
OBJECTS

DISTRESS

SCRATCH

CREATE AN ABSTRACT IN CHEWING GUM

SCOUR

STEAL LINES FROM FAMOUS POEMS.

. COMBINE THEM TO FORM YOUR OWN

DECORATE AN INSPIRATIONAL QUOTE.
Leave it for a stranger to find

let go of
something

Litter with letters

make this SOOTHE YOUR EYES

make this AGITATE YOUR EYES

UNFINISHED STORIES — WRITE ONLY THE FIRST LINE

_____

_____

_____

_____

_____

_____

_____

_____

_____

_____

tweet one #anti_journal

_____

Assign a COLOUR to each number on a DICE. ROLL IT. Paint. Repeat

USE THIS PAGE OF YOUR Anti JOURNAL to promote A WORTHWHILE CAUSE. HANG THIS IN A PUBLIC PLACE

Copy the pattern from a
favourite piece of clothing

Use a twig as a drawing tool

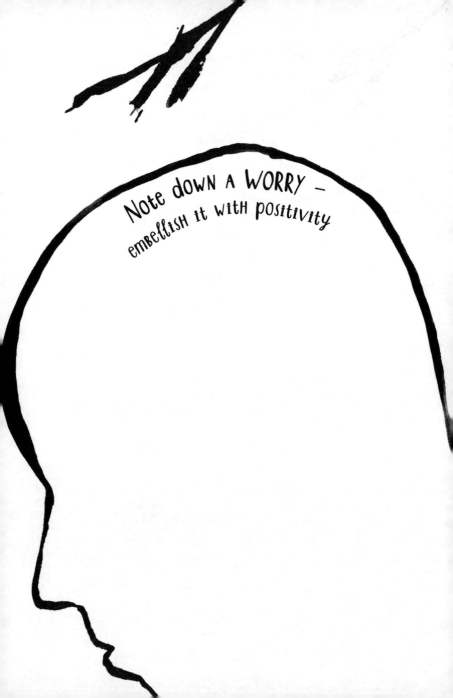

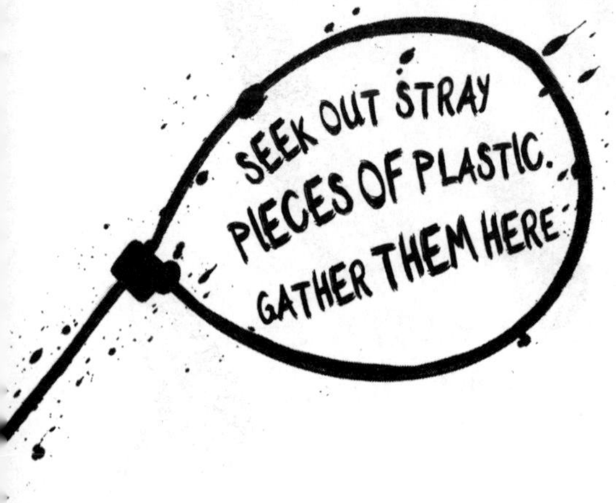
SEEK OUT STRAY
PIECES OF PLASTIC.
GATHER THEM HERE

MAKE THESE AS DIFFERENT
FROM EACH OTHER AS POSSIBLE

take the LONG ROUTE

ANY OBJECT YOU PLACE HERE
AUTOMATICALLY BECOMES A WORK OF ART

title it

DO NOT LOOK AT THIS

Sketch without looking at the page

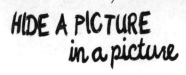

HIDE A PICTURE
in a picture

SCRUNCH this.
FiNd PATTERNS
iN the CREASES

PIXELATE
AN image

PAINT USING A
PLASTIC BUILDING BLOCK

Reclaim scraps from your waste-paper basket. Collage them here

USE
EVERY
PEN
YOU
CAN
FIND

REPEAT A POSITIVE STATEMENT
over and over

keep writing

keep writing

keep writing

Dump negativity

splice

together

images

in alternating

strips

ZOOM IN ON A
PART OF YOUR BODY

SPREAD anything spreadable

CREATE A SENSE OF MOVEMENT

CUT
THIS OFF

ENLARGE WHAT YOU SEE
OF A PREVIOUS ARTWORK

Use grass
to paint

Find a piece of useless information

decorate

swap this page
with a friend

SPRAY
HERE

Calm to

CHAOS

record a BLUR

through squinted eyes

FIND MINI ABSTRACTS

from close-ups and bits of other images

Ask a friend to sketch
YOU crudely

USE A PENCIL
IN AN UNUSUAL WAY

What if...................................

COMPLETE THE QUESTION   Picture it

Rip up
an item of
clothing you
haven't worn
for a while —
FRAY AND STAIN

PLAN the route from where you are
to where you'd like to be

(you are here)

ATTEMPT AN AMBITIOUS ARTWORK –
ABANDON IT HALFWAY THROUGH

1. CLASHING   4. BE BOLD
    2. PATTERNED   5. STICK SOMETHING ON
3. STRAY OUTSIDE THE LINES   6. SCRIBBLE

Copy a
part of
someone else's
Anti Journal

Dismantle an object
and use its parts

continue this...

FIND WONDER
IN NATURE

SKETCH OR PATTERN

Simplify it

Simplify it

Simplify it

Simplify it

Simplify it

BLEED COLOURS.
Place under
a dripping tap

design by
REMOVING
PARTS
OF THIS
PAGE

collage the
same shape
from different sources

Subtle differences in colour

DESIGN TRANSPARENTLY - reflect light

Message this to your phone-book or online contacts:

WHAT ARE YOU THINKING RIGHT NOW?
(THIS IS A SOCIAL EXPERIMENT FOR MY ANTI JOURNAL)

document what comes back:

Highlighter
pens

MAKE A MOVIE OF YOU turning the pages of your anti journal.

UPLOAD IT ONLINE

record FEEDBACK HERE,
good or BAD:

SQUASH something here.

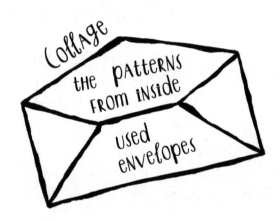

Collage the PATTERNS FROM iNSiDe used eNvelopes

A ONE-MINUTE DRAWING

ANTI-PAINT CHART

LABEL EACH SWATCH BY RANDOMLY SELECTING WORDS.
COLOUR EACH SWATCH AS THE WORD INSPIRES

DRAW WITH WORDS
WITH WORDS
DRAW WORDS
DRAW WITH WORDS draw draw WITH
WORDS DRAW WITH
DRAW WORDS WORDS
WITH WORDS WORDS DRAW
WITH WORDS DRAW

SMEAR!

DUNK

PUT YOUR PAINTBRUSH IN A PAIR OF COMPASSES

A crowd

OF

FOUND

FACES

DESCRIBE YOUR LIFE
IN TEN WORDS

_____

_____

_____

_____

_____

_____

_____

_____

_____

_____

add WORK or BILLS

release

tension

COVER AND CONCEAL
A MYSTERY OBJECT

REPRODUCE two pages of
your Anti JOURNAL in MINIATURE

leak ink
then tilt

GOOGLE MAP YOUR CHILDHOOD POSTCODE TURN IT INTO A PATCHWORK OF MEMORIES

Combine
people
you like
to create
one
individual

REPEAT ONE ACTION UNTIL
THE PAGE IS COVERED

CUT BAD NEWS FROM A NEWSPAPER AND MAKE SOMETHING HAPPY

SHRED AN IMAGE

Use puddles to
paint in NATURAL tones

show
individuality

CREATE CHARACTERFUL MARKS
Name each mark after someone
you know it suits best

name _____

name _____

name _____

name _____

name _____

name _____

PICTURE YOURSELF AS A tree

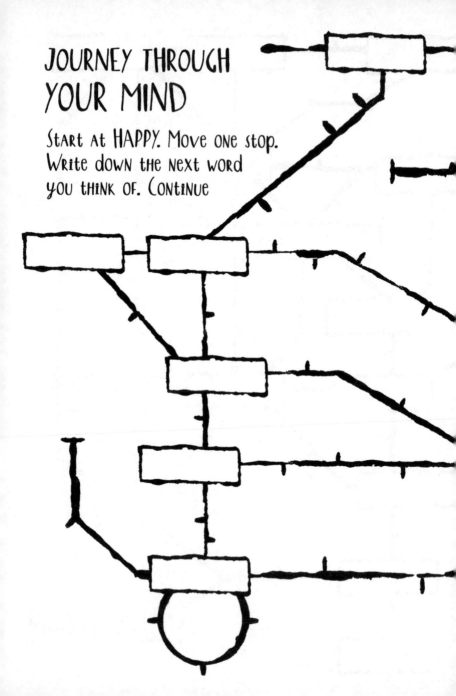

JOURNEY THROUGH YOUR MIND

Start at HAPPY. Move one stop.
Write down the next word
you think of. Continue

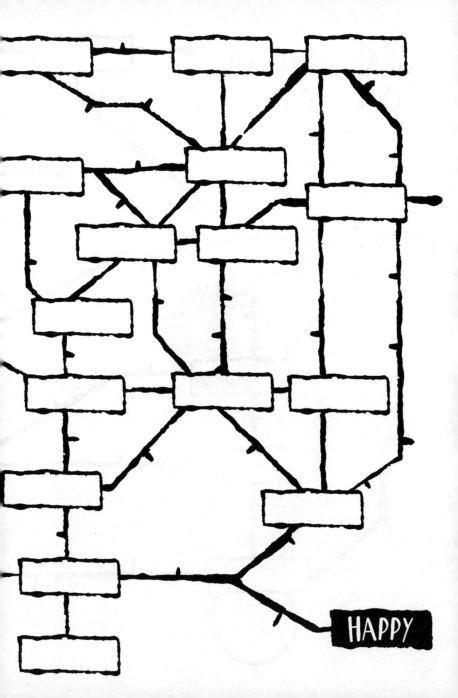

HAPPY

Make this
the centre of
Attention

Something FROM POPULAR CULTURE

you dislike

CUT UP AND SCATTERED

a photo

a photo of a photo

a photo of a photo of a photo

a photo of a photo of a photo of a photo

Go out into the world and
CREATE OUTRAGEOUSLY

share your ideas #anti_journal